SMALL WONDERS

THE FUNNY ANIMAL ART of FRANK FRAZETTA

Introduction by William Stout

KITCHEN SINK PRESS

ISBN 0-87816-146-5

Art by **Frank Frazetta**. Co-publishers: **Denis Kitchen** and **Greg Theakston**. Editor: **Greg Theakston**. Co-Editor: **Dave Schreiner**. Art Director, **Ray Fehrenbach**. Front cover art & color, and introduction: **William Stout**. Retouching: **Sean Leong**, **Scott Mitchell** and **Rob Stolzer**. Production: **Tammie Huenerberg**, **Diane Egbert** and **Bill Gregersen**. Back cover color: **Mario Macari**. Proofreading: **Doreen Riley.**

Watch for Volume Two of *Small Wonders: The Funny Animal Art of Frank Frazetta*, **in 1992.**

Library of Congress Cataloging-in-Publication Data
Frazetta, Frank.
   Small wonders -- the funny animal art of Frank Frazetta / by Frank Frazetta.
      p.   cm.
   ISBN 0-87816-146-5 : $9.95
   1. Comic books, strips, etc.--United States. 2. Animals--caricatures and cartoons. I. Title
   PN6726.F7   1991
   741.5'973--dc20   91-9719
                                                          CIP

Kitchen Sink Press publishes a full line of comics, books, and comics-related material. For a free catalog, write Kitchen Sink Press, No. 2 Swamp Rd., Princeton WI 54968.

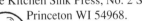

Introduction

by William Stout

Frank Frazetta is an artist primarily known for establishing *the* artistic style for science fiction paperback covers in the '60s, '70s and '80s, and for creating and defining the artistic and stylistic icons for the sf subgenre of sword-and-sorcery forever. But long before Frazetta breathed life back into Conan; before he, along with Roy Krenkel, brought about the Edgar Rice Burroughs boom of the early '60s; before his dazzling brushwork with Al Williamson in the EC comic books of the '50s...Frazetta was more often than not signing his name "Fritz" to a charming series of whimsical drawings for such comic book titles as *Barnyard Comics, Coo Coo Comics, Happy Comics* and *Goofy Comics* (not to be confused with the Disney character). In the parlance of the trade, these are known as funny animal comics. Frazetta's funny animal work serves as a crucial and revealing early glimpse inside his development as an artist.

The wartorn 1940s saw many movie studio animators supplementing their weekly incomes (around $25 from Warner Bros. to Disney's top of $90 to $100) by drawing funny animal comic books. Early on, a moonlighting artist who wrote, pencilled and inked his own stories made $15 a page; later the rate would rise to $25. Each artist produced a weekly base of ten pages, resulting in a "supplementary" income of $250 that vastly surpassed his wage at the studio. Fast artists like Ken Hultgren averaged 30 pages a week.

The same elements of drawing, character design, and storytelling from their work in animated shorts were easily transferred to the printed page. For the most part, the work was drawn well, but with little of the character development that characterized the critters inhabiting the movie screens.

In Los Angeles, an entrepreneur named Jim Davis acted as an agent for the animators. The group included the three Karp brothers and Ken Hultgren from Disney; and Ken Champin, Manuel Perez, Ed Dunn, Hawley Pratt, Jack Bradbury and Don R. Christensen ("Don Arr") from Warners. Doing work for Standard Comics was a happy social affair, with Davis doling out assignments and receiving finished pages at jovial noontime lunches at Warner Brothers. Davis had no editorial input; he just shipped the work back east to editor Richard Hughes (who wrote most of the "Super Mouse" stories) and took care of promptly paying the guys. Davis also promoted the artists' talents outside comic books. At one point he secured a contract for technical drawings from Lockheed. He turned these same animators, many of whom had never seen isometric perspectives before, loose on the project.

The group operated as a mutual admiration society, each artist envying the particular strengths they saw in the others' work. Hultgren, for example, was considered with a fair amount of awe for being the "fastest inker in the business." The camaraderie was in marked contrast to the social isolation of the men's later work for Western Publishing ("Dell"), where their only get-together would be at the company Christmas party. Besides the advantage of extra pay, the animators had the freedom to work at home and on their own schedules.

In 1947, at the age of 19, Frazetta arrived on these same funny animal pages still close to his classical art training under Michael Falanga. Frank Frazetta's background, and hence his work, differed from that of his colleagues. Two simultaneous dynamics occurred during Frazetta's funny animal days that changed him as an artist forever.

"Graham Ingels took me on at Standard," he recalls. "He saw some potential in my work. Graham had some problems, though, and quit, and Ralph Mayo took over. Ralph was a real student of art, and he also saw my potential. He coddled me and fed me artistically. He once told me that if I could learn anatomy, it would make all the difference in the world. He gave me a couple of big anatomy books to study over the years. I took both copies home and copied each and every page that night. The next day I returned and out of sheer innocence and pride I proclaimed, 'Now I know anatomy!' 'Wait,' Mayo said, 'I've been studying it for over 15 years and *I* don't know anatomy!' That was the only real study of anatomy that I ever made. I retained about 50 to 60 per cent of the knowledge from that overnight crash course."

It was an important transitional moment for the young artist.

"Before, I used to *guess* at the anatomy of figures. Suddenly, I *knew*. The arms, the legs, the torsos were all far more impressive now that they had that knowledge behind them. I lost my consciousness of other artists' styles and became focused on my own."

The work of Harold Foster in the *Tarzan* and *Prince Valiant* Sunday newspaper strips was a major influence on the young Frazetta as a comics artist. The influence is especially evident in a story from *Happy Comics* titled "Diamonds to Pebbles". The handsome prince of the story bears an uncanny resemblance to Foster's Prince Valiant and the heroine is a dead ringer for Val's great love, Aleta.

"Foster was my first big comics influence. Then I was swept up by [Milton] Caniff; Caniff was a god at the time. But I eventually realized this direction wasn't Frazetta. So I rediscovered Foster and realism, and that was the real turning point for me. That was when the real me came through, and I began the pursuit of my own personal vision."

Frazetta's physical exaggeration of each animal's characteristics went far beyond the homogenized (or "Disneyfied") effort that reflected the roots of the animators' day jobs. This is not meant to denigrate that work; for the most part, each of their drawings could comfortably fit within the Walter Foster Animation manuals by Preston Blair as good examples of animation drawing. In fact, Hultgren was the author and illustrator of the outstanding book *The Art of Animal Drawing-Construction/Action Analysis/Caricature*. It must also be noted that the financial nature and the constraints of the animation medium itself forced this sameness upon its artists, and that even within those restrictions, individual lights still shone through. Disney's famous "nine old men" serve as classic examples.

"I was aware of the other guys in the books," Frazetta said. "Yeah, they were good guys."

And they were aware of him. The powers at Disney were so impressed with Frazetta's work that he received an offer to come out to Hollywood (Burbank, actually) to work for the studio. Frazetta was quite flattered—he keeps the letter to this day—but felt it was out of the question for him to make the California move. He'd have to leave his parents and his beloved Brooklyn Dodgers behind.

Frazetta had other fans of his funny animal art. Once, during lean times, his landlady accepted a beautiful funny animal piece in lieu of a month's rent.

Much of Frazetta's work in the funny animal genre functioned as illustrations to one page text stories. Unlike his contemporaries, Frazetta's work did not look like segments of storyboards from an animated cartoon. His drawings for the few actual comic book stories he drew for these magazines also retained this illustrational quality and stood out from the rest of the work in the book. This effect was further enhanced by the aesthetic lettering of Howard Ferguson, who is primarily known as Joe Simon and Jack Kirby's key letterer during their "golden age". Ferguson holds the distinction of lettering Frazetta's first story for comic books, the "Snowman" story in *Talley Ho Comics*.

As good as his work was in these books, and as hard as he worked, Frazetta still encountered a certain amount of frustration.

"They had me doing funny animal work because they felt I wasn't ready to do the straight stuff. I was *far* more fascinated with the straight stuff."

The sometimes elaborate Frazetta brush rendering evoked a different sense than did the sleekly animatable bare-essence drawings of his older contemporaries.

"I never used reference for the animals. I just did what the animators did and remembered my impressions of those animals. I felt the Disney approach was rather boring, so I would draw them real and then distort them, and then render them as they really looked. I tried to produce work that was not necessarily correct, but *believable* — work that grabbed you emotionally. That's the fun thing to do, while making it as accurate as you can."

Frazetta's little critters and bears ("Bruno Bear" and "Talented Bear") actually had fur. His fine brushwork was particularly evident in his wolves — see "City Cousin". His trees were not plastic symbols; they had bark and individual character ("The Strange Little Creature" and "Spare That Tree"). There was also a dark territory traveled by Frazetta that was explored in the feature film work of the animators, but that was never hinted at in their comic book work. Frazetta's wolves were not merely the slyly mischievous lupine characters from a children's cartoon; they hungrily stared out from the pages with death in their eyes, as in "The Rabbit Who Wouldn't Run", "Nubby the Lamb" and "Coalie the Lamb".

Traces of his interest in the subject matter that would later help to catapult him to fame are interlaced through all his funny animal work. His cute bunnies and kittens scampered over moss-encrusted logs studded with an abundance of his trademarked mushrooms ("The Talkative Mouse", "Eager Beaver", "Abbott the Rabbit"). Lush and gnarled vegetation gave shelter to lily pad-laden ponds ("Ferdinand the Bullfrog", "Hardback Softheart", "Wishful Willy"). Tarzan's jungles grace "Flippy the Monk".

In contrast to the light and airy drawings of the animators, Frazetta's work was often thick with mood ("Nibby", "Unhappy Animal",

"Wandering Kitten"), boasting a powerful use of blacks. His careful attention to detail and fairy tale whimsy produced dreamy weeping willows that framed houses whose roofs dripped down from hooded peaks ("The Quiet Pup", page 4 of "Barney's Little Helper" and the nightmarish flipside of that image, "The Ghost"). "Herbie" sports a flower garden to rival those drawn by the English children's book illustrator Charles Robinson. Nearly all of the above elements were brought into play by Frazetta in a little untitled two page "Hucky Duck" gem from *Barnyard Comics #25*, in which Hucky encounters Kid Temptation.

Even at such an early age, Frazetta was broadly successful at expressing the character and essence of a large variety of animals.

"The detail is far less important to me than the whole work: the design, the composition, the color, the emotional impact of the thing. It drives me nuts when people focus on the detail. They're missing out on what *really* makes my art work."

There is little to criticize in Frazetta's funny animal work. There's a blandness of character and design to most of his fish; but then, very few fish have expressive personalities. And in his illustration that accompanies "The Walking Stick", the stick has far more charm than the little sparrow it confronts. On the other hand, he could take the characters of Hucky Duck and Barney Rooster — characters created by other artists — and broadly expand them.

Although his funny animal drawings may never gain him the notoriety and fame of the Burroughs and "Conan" paintings, this work lives as one of the most significant and illuminating chapters in the history of this influential artist.

"I'm just a straight, ordinary guy. I *truly* wish the world was full of sweetness, flowers and happiness. But it's not, and I do reveal that dark side in some of my work. I am known for my violent stuff.

"But the funny stuff is the *real* me."

I would like to thank Frank Frazetta, Don R. Christensen and Jack Bradbury for their generous help in providing information, background and reminiscences about their old "Funny Animal Days". Greg Theakston and Robert R. Barrett provided additional information.

Noted illustrator William Stout is currently working on storyboards for movies.

SNOWMAN

by JOHN GIUNTA AND FRANK FRAZETTA

DESOLATION ISLAND... THE LAST REFUGE ON EARTH FOR THE HUNTED HUMANS THAT SOCIETY HAS CAST OFF AS LEECHES TO HUMANITY! IT IS AN ISLAND OF HORROR... ONLY THE FACES OF ITS INHABITANTS OUTDO THE UTTER GLOOM OF THE SCENE...

LETTERING DESIGNS by H.O. FERGUSON

THE *IDIOT!* LEAVING ME NEAR JAGGED ICE...WHICH CAN EASILY CUT MY BONDS...*THE FOOL!*

LOOK! COMRADES— THE EVIL ONE IS UNLEASHING DREAD MAGIC!

SEE! A SEA SERPENT! IT IS ABOUT TO ATTACK THE SHIP!

IT IS THE END OF MY ENEMY! BUT WHAT'S THIS? *NATIVE* ENEMIES! I'LL SOON ATTEND TO THEM!

I COMMAND THAT AN ARMY OF SAVAGES FOLLOW ME AND MY WISHES! *GOOD!!* FOLLOW ME!

IN A MATTER OF MINUTES...CHAOS!

OH, MIGHTY ONE... SAVE US IN OUR TIME OF NEED! WREAK HAVOC ON OUR INVADERS! WE IMPLORE YOU...

*S*UDDENLY A STRANGE THING OCCURS... FOR FROM THE ICY STATUE LIKE FIGURE, A FORM TAKES SHAPE... A FIGURE OF ACTION AND REVENGE... IT IS THE BIRTH OF *SNOWMAN!*

HOW LONG DID THIS FANG CHARACTER EXPECT ME TO REMAIN AN IDOL? *I'LL MOW 'IM DOWN!*

3

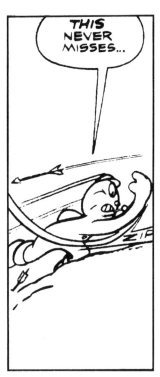

BARNEY ROOSTER

I WANT TO SEND A WIRE TO SNOOZE! "COME TO CITY AT ONCE. YOUR UNCLE WOOF GOING TO DOGS AGAIN." SIGNED... AUNTIE.

THAT'LL BE 25¢!

A RIDICULOUS DEMAND, MY GOOD MAN! SEND IT "COLLECT."

TELEGRAM FOR SNOOZE. SIGN HERE.

TELEGRAM, HUH? THIS FAST PACE IS KILLIN' ME!

HO-HUM!

I GOTTA GO TO THE CITY, PROFESSOR.

WELL, IF YOU HAVE TO GO, I GUESS YOU'LL HAVE TO, BUT WHO IS GOING TO GUARD THE CORN?

I'LL GET A SUBSTITUTE TO WATCH IT WHILE I'M GONE.

ALRIGHT, BUT BE SURE HE'S CAPABLE. DON'T GET ANYONE ANY DUMBER THAN YOURSELF!

DON'T WORRY, I DON'T KNOW ANYONE DUMBER THAN ME. THIS GUY'S THE CAT'S WHISKERS ...HE WEARS 'EM EVEN!

HMM... I WONDER IF I SHOULD HAVE SAID THAT?

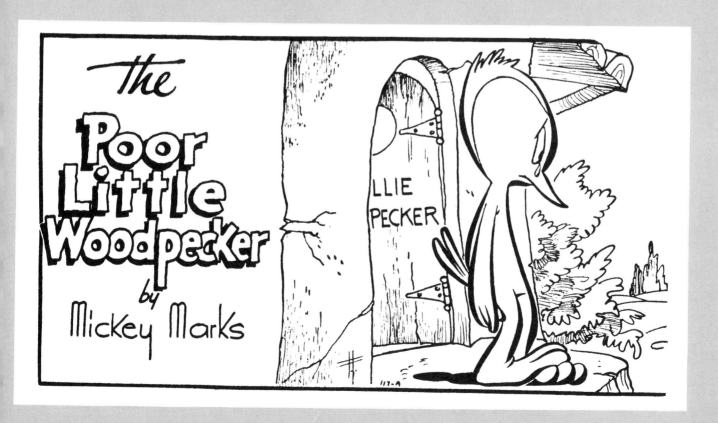

The Timid Caterpillar

By Betty Cummings

3

The BIG BADGER HUNT

By Justin Blazer

A 105

BARNYARD HERO

By Pat Cherr

A-200

The Colt Who Was Too Good

By Betty Cummings

A-493

NOTHING AT ALL

By Elizabeth Starr

The NIGHTINGALE Who Couldn't Sing

By Betty Cummings

The WALKING STICK

By Mickey Marks

Lucky BIRD

by Donald Bayne Hobart

HUCKY DUCK

"Circus Ticket"

BUT MA... I JUST GOTTA HAVE FIFTY CENTS. THE CIRCUS IS COMING TOMORROW AND I JUST GOTTA BUY A TICKET!

YOU SHOULD HAVE SAVED FROM YOUR ALLOWANCE! IF YOU WANT FIFTY CENTS GO OUT AND EARN IT!

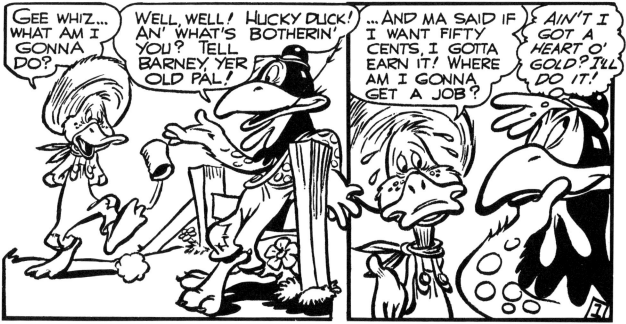

GEE WHIZ... WHAT AM I GONNA DO?

WELL, WELL! HUCKY DUCK! AN' WHAT'S BOTHERIN' YOU? TELL BARNEY, YER OLD PAL!

...AND MA SAID IF I WANT FIFTY CENTS, I GOTTA EARN IT! WHERE AM I GONNA GET A JOB?

AIN'T I GOT A HEART O' GOLD? I'LL DO IT!

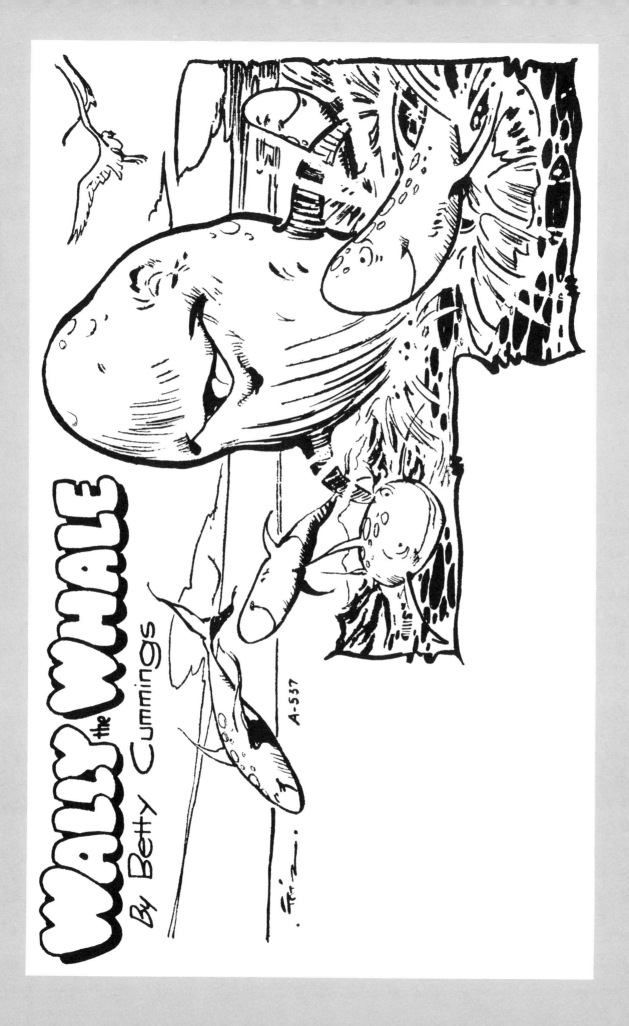

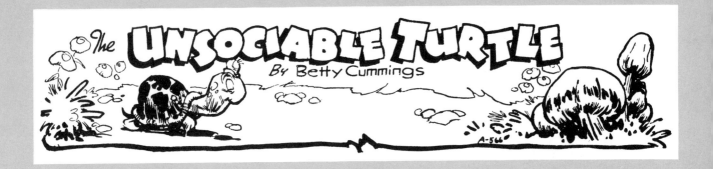